ALEX GRAHAM'S

FRED BASSET 2000

Orion Books Ltd
Orion House
5 Upper St Martin's Lane
London WC2H 9EA

First published by Orion in 2000

Drawings by Michael Martin

Cover illustrations by Alex Graham

© Associated Newspapers plc 2000

ISBN 0 75283 766 4

Printed and bound in Great Britain
by The Guernsey Press Limited

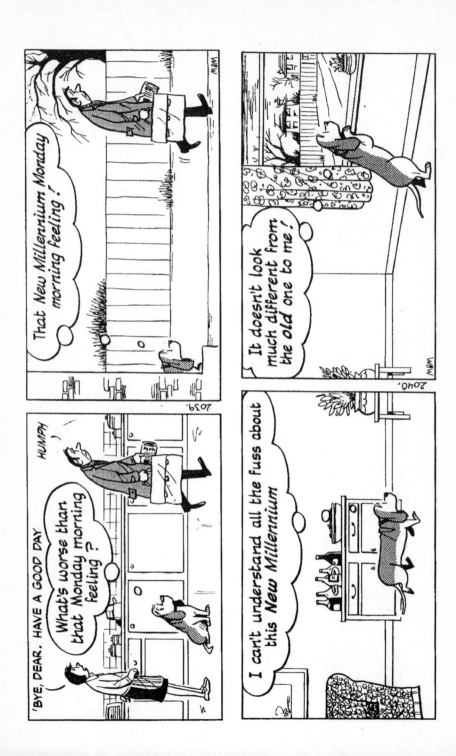

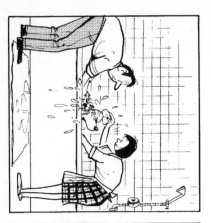

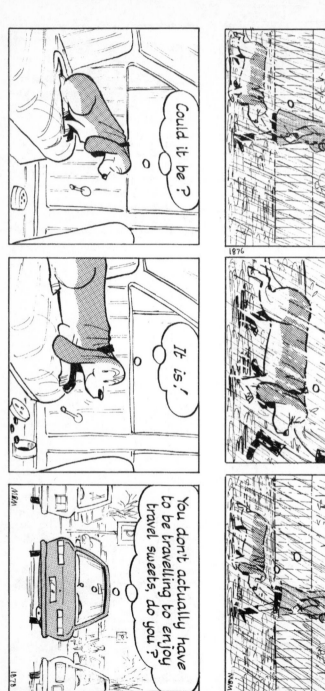

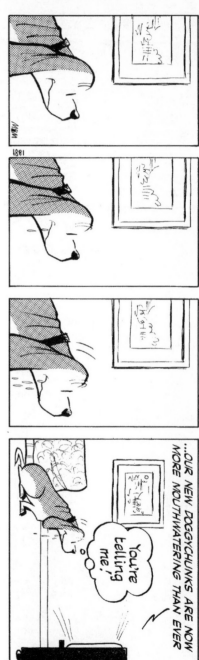

1883

1884

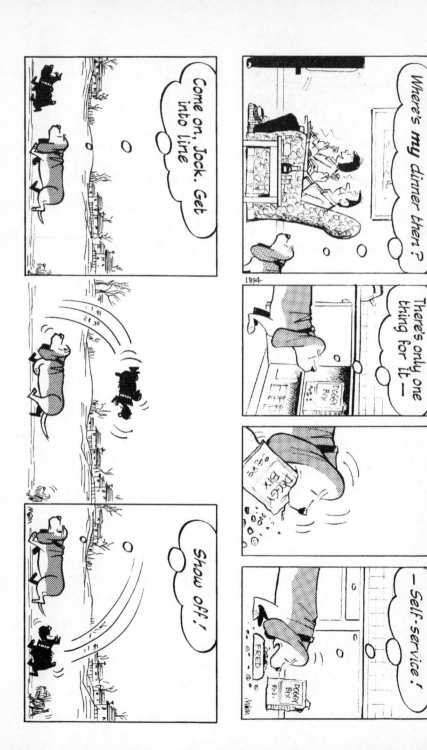

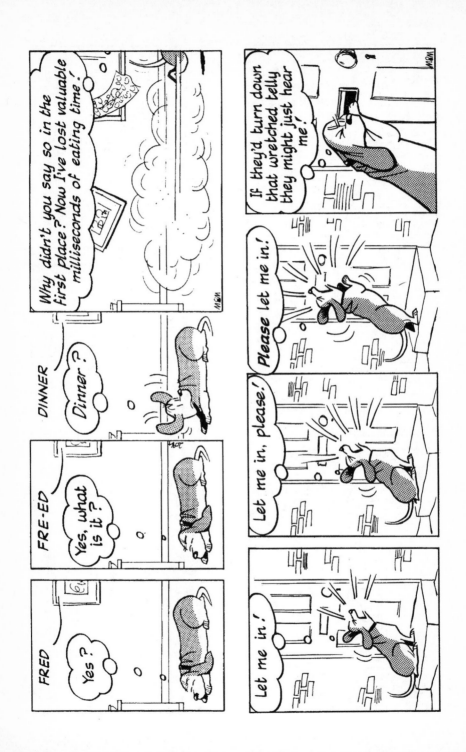

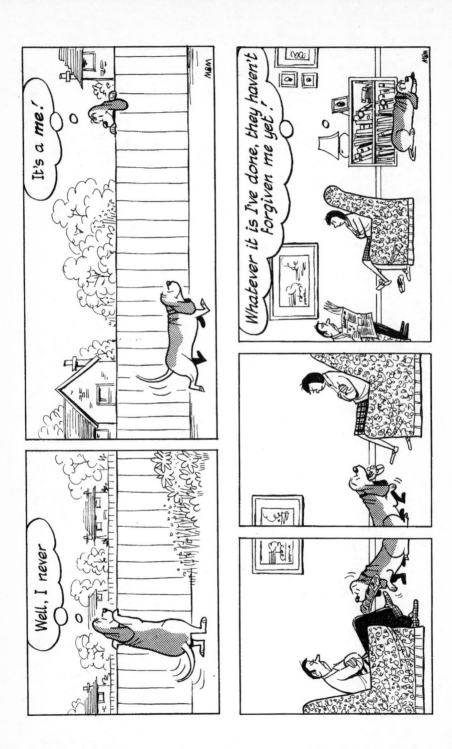

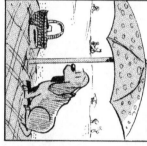

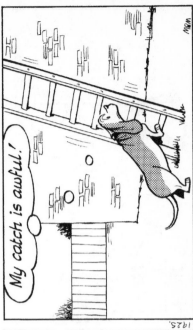

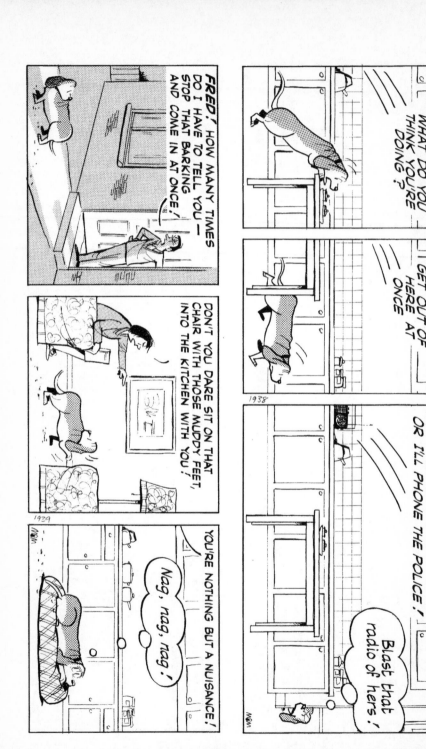

Little Sam seems to have got something he hasn't....

1946

...the knack!

'Ah, my horoscope!' — 'A time to relax, unwind and let the busy world around you float by.'

1947

Funnily enough...

...that's exactly what I had in mind!

1957

1958

They look rather comfy

1959

Room for one more?

YOU'RE LATE! WHERE HAVE YOU BEEN?

I BUMPED INTO ANGELA...

...AND WE POPPED INTO THE CHEQUERS FOR A DRINK

CHEQUERS?

— DRINK?

1960.

...YES, WE EVEN HAD A FEW GAMES OF DARTS

You're not the only one who can have a drink and a game of darts at The Chequers, you know!

DARTS?

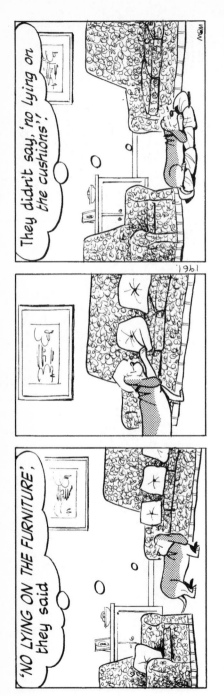

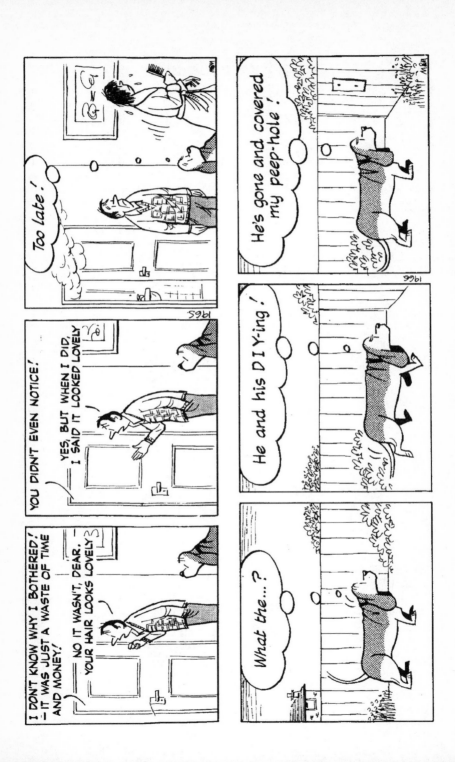

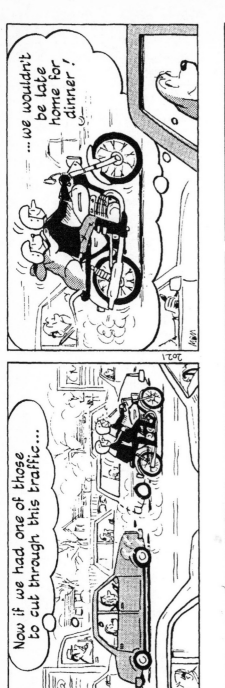

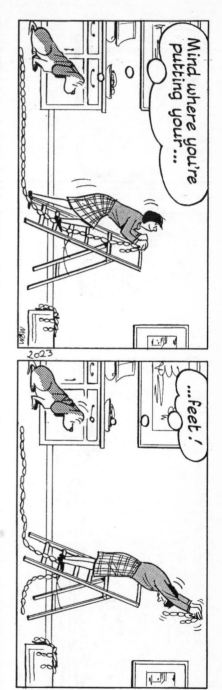

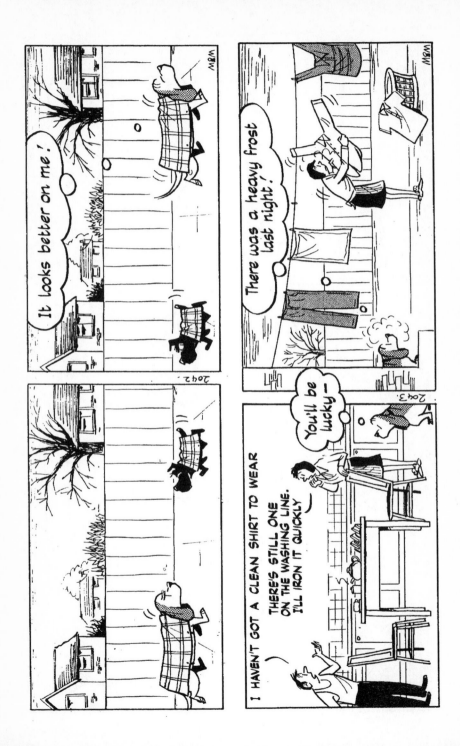

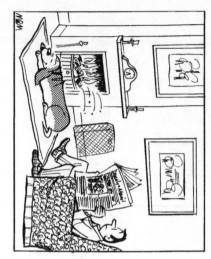

Ouch!

2052.

2053.

Yorky's the only dog I know that can get out of his depth in a puddle!

Could you put up the fireguard, please?

...another treble twenty —and another—

One hundred and eighty!

Actually, it was a two, a five and a double one. I was just trying to liven up the evening.

2056.

With this bitter north wind...

...I take my daily exercise in moderation.

2057.

2061

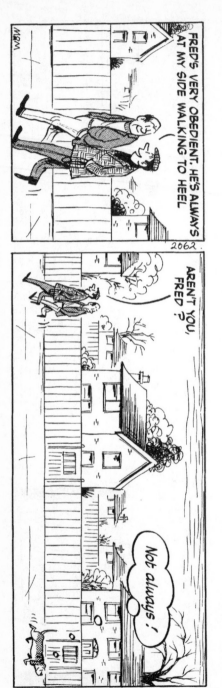

2062

2066.

2065.

We're just trying out a new candidate for our gang

Taffy, would you like to take the lead for a while?

Cutlets from Mr Brown the butcher, eh?

We think it's important for a new member not to feel left out. For him to be able to stride off in front and see our patch for himself...

2070.

OK, Taffy! You're in!

...and to check the coast is clear when passing Satan's place!

BEWARE FIERCE DOG

2069.

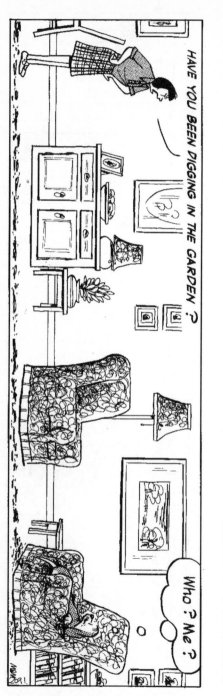

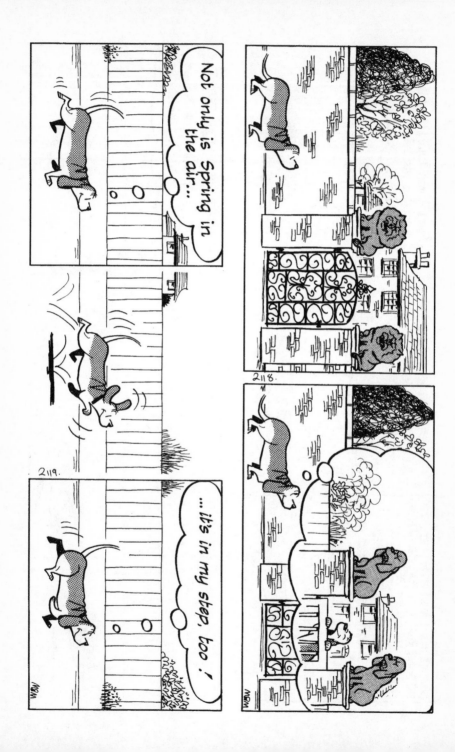